CAROLS OF TODAY

SEVENTEEN ORIGINAL SETTINGS
FOR MIXED VOICES

1368

MUSIC DEPARTMENT

OXFORD UNIVERSITY PRESS

44 CONDUIT STREET   417 FIFTH AVENUE
LONDON W.1   NEW YORK 16 N.Y.

CONTENTS

Where first lines differ from titles, the former are shown in italics

* = Unaccompanied,   † = optional organ

All carols are for Christmas unless otherwise indicated

Most of the contents of this collection will appear on a double-sided LP record to be released by Argo (Stereo ZRG 5499; Mono RG 499) in Autumn 1966.

CAROLS OF TODAY

1. WHAT TIDINGS?

Words by John Audelay (15th.c.)
adapted by Jacqueline Froom

ALUN HODDINOTT
(Op. 38)

© Oxford University Press 1965

Printed in Great Britain

2. A seem - ly sight it is__ to see:__ The maid__ that hath__ this ba - by borne__ Con - ceived__ a lord of high__ de - gree,__ And maid - en is__ as was be - fore. Such won - drous ti - dings ye may hear: That God and man is one on earth, Brought to us by this won - drous birth.

3. A won - drous thing has now__ be - fall:__ That lord__ that made__ both sea__ and sun,__ Heav'n__ and earth__ and an - gels all, In

man - kind_ is now be-come. What ti - dings bring you, mes - sen - ger?

Now God and man is one on earth, Brought to us by this won-drous birth.

4. That lord_ that all thing made_ of nought_ Is man_ be - come_ for

man - kind's love, _ For with his blood he shall _ be brought_ From

woe_ to bliss_ that is a - bove. Such won - drous ti - dings ye may hear:

Now God and man is one on earth, Brought to us by this won - drous birth.

2. A LITTLE CHILD THERE IS YBORN

(S. A. T. B. Soli and Chorus)

15th century anonymous words

JOHN JOUBERT
(Op. 48)

Words from *The Oxford Book of Carols* by permission

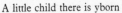

continued overleaf

For the Birmingham Singers' Club

3. ALLELUYA, A NEW WORK IS COME ON HAN

15th century anonymous words

PETER WISHA

- ya, al - le - lu - ya, al - le - lu -

al - le - lu - ya, al - le - lu - ya,

- ya, al - le - lu - ya, al - le - lu -

al - le - lu - ya, al - le - lu - ya,

- ya, al - le - lu -

- ya, al - le - lu -

- ya, al - le - lu - ya, al - le - lu - ya.

al - le - lu - ya, al - le - lu - ya.

- ya, al - le - lu - ya, al - le - lu - ya.

al - le - lu - ya, al - le - lu - ya.

- ya, al - le - lu - ya.   1. A new work is come on

- ya, al - le - lu - ya.   1. A new work is come on

4. AVE PLENA GRACIA

(S.A.T. soli and S.A.T.B. chorus with opt. organ)

15th century anonymous words
PETER MAXWELL DAVIES

★The organ part, when used, should not merely "double" the voices, but add a bright silvery sparkle to them, the registration approximating as nearly as practicable that of an eighteenth-century chamber organ.

The music is published by arrangement with Messrs. Boosey & Hawkes Ltd.

Tempo I

FULL

A - ve, a - ve ple - na gra - ci - a,___ A - ve, De - i

A - ve, a - ve ple - na___ gra - ci - a, A - ve, De - i

Organ

poco rit. _ _ _ - **Tempo II**

SOLI

ma -ter Ma - ri - a.___ 2. Hail_ be thou, Queen of pa -ra - dise, Of all wo-

ma -ter Ma - ri - a.___ 2. Hail_ be thou, Queen of pa -ra - dise, Of all wo -

poco rit. _ _ _ _ **Tempo II**

- men thou bear-ës price, Ma - ri - a.___ Hail wife, hail mai-dë bright_ of

- men_ thou_ bear - ës price, Ma - ri - a.___ Hail wife, hail mai-dë bright_ of

poco rit. _ _ _

ble!_ Hail daugh-ter, hail sis - ter full of pi - ty! Ma - ri - a.___

ble! _ Hail daugh-ter, hail sis - ter full of___ pi - ty! Ma - ri - a.___

continued overleaf

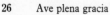

Tempo II
SOLI

3. Thou art em-përess of hea-ven free; Now art thou mo-der in

3. Thou art em-përess of hea - ven free; Now art thou mo-der in

3. Thou art em-përess of hea - ven free; Now art thou mo-der in

Tempo II

poco rit. _ _ _ _   **Tempo II**

ma - jes - ty,_ Ma - ri - a._ Thou pray for us un - to thy

_ ma - jes - ty, Ma - ri - a._ Thou pray for us un - to thy

_ ma - jes - ty,_ Ma - ri - a._ Thou pray for us un - to thy_

poco rit. _ _ _ _   **Tempo II**

poco rit._ _ _ _

Son,_ In hea - ven bliss that we may wone,_ Ma - ri - a._

Son,_ In hea-ven bliss that we_ may wone,_ Ma - ri - a._

Son, In hea - ven_ bliss that we_ may wone, Ma - ri - a._

poco rit._ _ _ _

continued overleaf

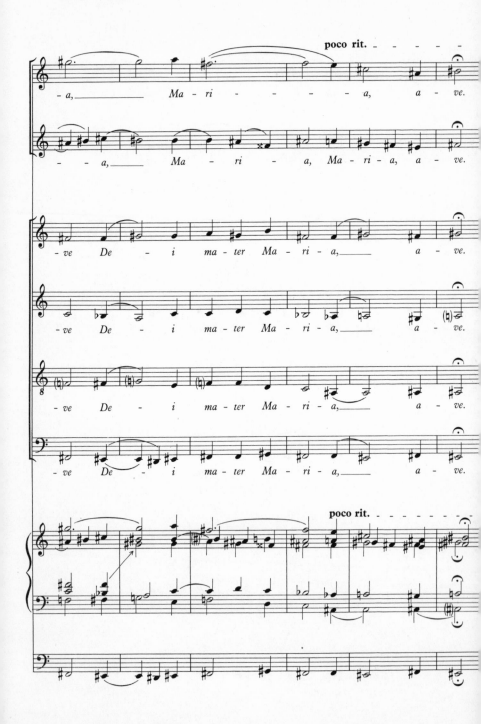

To C.H.W.

5. THE OXEN

Words by
THOMAS HARDY

ALAN RAWSTHORNE

Words from *The Collected Poems of Thomas Hardy* by permission of the Trustees of the Hardy Estate and of Messrs. Macmillan & Co. Ltd.

36

6. THE SHOUT

An Easter Carol

Words by
ADAM FOX

JOHN GARDNER
(Op. 67)

© Oxford University Press 1965 (Words and music)

7. JESU, AS THOU ART OUR SAVIOUR

5th century anonymous words

BENJAMIN BRITTEN

★or soprano solo or semi-chorus.   †Use Latin pronunciation throughout—'Yaysoo'

This is Variation III of the Choral Variations *A Boy was Born* (O.U.P.)

The words from *Ancient English Christmas Carols*, collected and arranged by Edith Rickert, are reprinted by her kind permission and that of the publishers, Messrs. Chatto and Windus.

8. LAETABUNDUS

(Carol in two parts★)

11th century anonymous words

GORDON CROSS

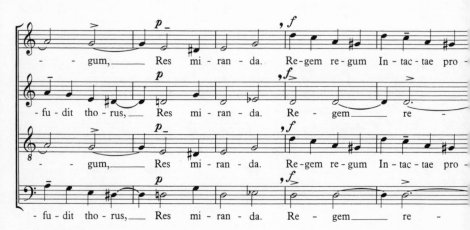

★ May be sung S.A., T.B., S.T.B., or S.A.T.B. (if S.A.T.B. all may sing v. 1 and Refrain, women singing remaining verses).
† If sung S.A. as many altos as can may sing with sopranos.

-fu - dit tho - rus, Res mi - ran - da, res mi - ran - da.

mf

- gum, Res mi - ran - da res, res mi - ran - da.

mf

-fu - dit tho - rus, Res mi - ran - da, res mi - ran - da.

mf

- gum, Res mi - ran - da, res, res mi - ran - da.

mf

f

Lae - ta - bun - dus Ex - sul - tet fi - de - lis cho - rus;___ Al - le - lu -

f

Lae - ta - bun - dus Ex - sul - tet fi - de - lis cho - rus;___ Al - le - lu -

p   *f*

- ia, Al - le - lu - ia, Al - le - lu - ia.

p   *f*

Al - le - lu - ia, Al - le - lu - ia.

p   *f*

- ia, Al - le - lu - ia, Al - le - lu - ia.

p   *f*

Al - le - lu - ia, Al - le - lu - ia.

S. **Più sostenuto**

p

3. An - ge - lus con - si - li - i Na - tus est de vir - gi - ne,

T.

p

3. An - ge - lus con - si - li - i Na - tus est de vir - gi - ne,

S. Sol de stel - la; Al - le - lu - ia. 4. Sol oc - cas - um
A. Sol de stel - la;____ Al - le - lu - ia. 4. Sol oc - cas - um
T. Sol de stel - la; Al - le - lu - ia. 4. Sol oc - cas - um
B. [or 8ve bassa] Sol de stel - la;____ Al - le - lu - ia. [or 8ve bassa] 4. Sol oc - cas - um

nes - ci - ens Stel - la sem - per ru - ti - lans Sem - per cla - ra,
nes - ci - ens Stel - la sem - per ru - ti - lans Sem - per cla - ra,
nes - ci - ens Stel - la sem - per ru - ti - lans Sem - per cla - ra,
nes - ci - ens Stel - la sem - per ru - ti - lans Sem - per cla - ra.

% Allegro vigoroso

sem - per cla - ra. Lae - ta - bun - dus Ex - sul - tet fi - de - lis cho - rus
sem - per cla - ra.____ La____
sem - per cla - ra. Lae - ta - bun - dus Ex - sul - tet fi - de - lis cho - rus
sem - per cla - ra.____ La____

Dal 𝄋 al

Let the faithful choir sing Alleluia. A virgin's bed has brought forth the king of kings, a wondrous thing. The Angel of council is born of a virgin — the sun from a star; a sun that knows no setting, a star that is always shining, always bright. As a star puts forth its ray, so the virgin puts forth her son in like manner. The star does not lose virtue by giving forth its ray, or the mother by bearing a son. Gaze on the child whom holy writ fortells. A maiden has given birth to him.

9. COVENTRY CAROL

15th century anonymous words

JOHN McCABE

Charg-ed he hath this day His men of might, In his

That woe is me, Poor child for

own sight, All young child-ren to slay.

Tempo primo (♩ = c. 76)

molto espressivo

molto rit.

sfzpp sub.

molto rit.

Tempo primo (♩ = c. 76)

pp

Man.

diminuendo

thee! And ev - er morn and day, For thy part - ing Nei-ther

10. THE SORROWS OF MARY

15th century anonymous words   RICHARD RODNEY BENNETT

The music is published by arrangement with Universal Edition (London) Ltd.

rit.

-filled_ with_ pain most_ pi - te-ous - ly.'_____

Tempo I (meno mosso)

Ma - ry, mo-ther, grieve_____ you not ill. From

heav'n he came this_____ to ful - fil. _____ Be

- cause man - kind it should_____ not spill, He_____

took his death with per - - - fect good - will.

11. WASSAIL CAROL

16th century anonymous words

WILLIAM MATHIAS
(Opus 26, No. 1)

Source of words: Balliol College, Oxford, MS. 354, printed in *The Early English Carols* (Greene)

© Oxford University Press 1965

Printed in Great Britain

That one God is in Tri - ni - ty, Fa - ther of Heaven, of might-ès most.

2. And joy to the vir - gin pure That ev - er kept_ her un - de-filed,

Ground-ed in grace,_ in heart_ full sure, And bare_ a child as maid-en mild.

Ped.

Ah

That shone_ three king - ès

3. Beth - le - hem and the star_ so shen,★

(ah)

for to guide,   The king - ès three off -

Bear wit - ness of this_ maid - en clean;

(ah)

- ered that tide.   4. And shep - herds heard, as

★"shen," pronounced "sheen" = "bright"

an - gel's voice_ it was out rung._____ 5. Now

joy be to the bless - ed - ful child, And joy__ be to__ his

mo - ther dear;____ Joy we all of that maid - en mild, And

12. BALULALOW

Words: WEDDERBURN, 1567

NICHOLAS MAW

The music is published by arrangement with Messrs. Boosey & Hawkes Ltd.

The words are from 'Ane Sang of the birth of Christ' ('I come from heaven to tell'), a piece of fifteen stanzas, from *Ane Compendious Buik of Godly and Spirituall Sangis*, 1567, by the brothers James, John, and Robert Wedderburn. The whole poem is a translation of the Christmas Eve Carol which Luther wrote for his son Hans, 'Von Himmel hoch', first published in *Geistliche Lieder*, 1535.

†The first alto part may be sung by a few sopranos

To my god-daughter Rebekah Phibbs

13. POOR WORLD — PROUD WORLD

RICHARD CRASHAW
(? 1613-1649)

ADRIAN CRUFT
(Op. 41)

14. MAKE YE MERRY FOR HIM THAT IS COME

15th century anonymous words

IMOGEN HOLST

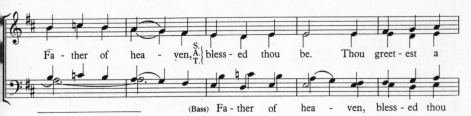

15. ON CHRISTMAS DAY

Words by
THOMAS TRAHERNE
(Verses 1, 2, 4, 8)

DAVID BLAKE

Duration c. 4' 20''

See how each one the o - ther

-ther calls To fix his I - vy on the walls,

_____ fix his I - vy on the walls,

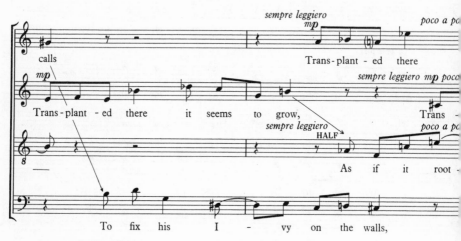

calls

Trans - plant - ed there

Trans-plant - ed there it seems to grow,

Trans -

_____

As if it root -

To fix his I - vy on the walls,

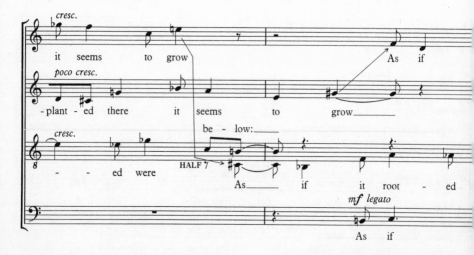

it seems to grow

As if

-plant - ed there it seems to grow_____

_____ ed were

be - low:_____

As_____ if it root - ed

As if

16. THE VIRGIN AND CHILD

15th century anonymous words
(adapted)

PHYLLIS TAT[E]

★To be sung without *rallentando* until page 105

†The notes between square brackets in the alto part should be sung by second sopranos when male altos use their optional alternative small notes.

Note: 'Ped.' refers to organ

© Oxford University Press 1965

be not King ve - ray;★ But, ne'er -the - less, I will not cease To

sing____ by by, lul - lay.'

2. The

Ped. (uncpld.)
Ped. (cpld.)
(Piano 8ve lower)

child then spake; in his talk -ing He____ to his mo -ther said: 'It

mp cantabile
Man.

Ped.

★ veray = in truth

★ light = quick

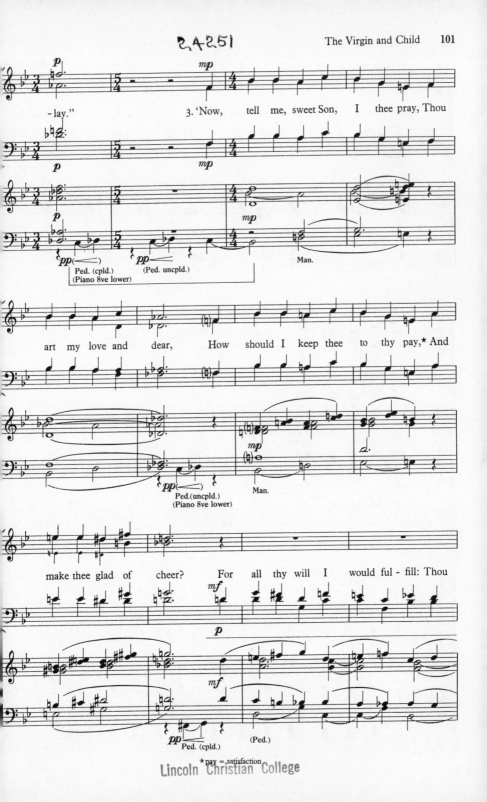

* pay = satisfaction

- lay."''

5. 'Now   sweet   Son,   since   it   is   so   All

things   are   at   thy   will,   I   pray thee grant   to   me   a   boon,   If

it   be   right   and   skill.★   That   child   or   man   That   will   or   can,   Be

★skill = reasonable

For Louis Halsey and the Elizabethan Singers

17. IN EXCELSIS GLORIA

15th century anonymous words

P. RACINE FRICKER

For rehearsal only